MASTERPIECES

of

PIANO MUSIC

The largest and most comprehensive collection of standard piano compositions ever published, covering completely all fields of classic, modern, light and operatic piano music :: ::

Selected and Edited by

ALBERT E. WIER

MUMIL PUBLISHING CO.
INCORPORATED

NEW YORK

Printed in the United States of America

PREFACE

LOVERS of standard piano music have long awaited a collection which would cover comprehensively all the important fields of musical composition, including classical, modern, light and operatic selections. In this book they will find their ideals fully realized, as its scope is practically unlimited, and the number as well as variety of compositions unequalled in any previous publication of the kind.

It may be truthfully said that the possessor of "Masterpieces of Piano Music" has within it all the standard compositions one would care to permanently possess, and, as more and more use is made of its pages, there will come a fuller realization of how completely and efficiently the editor has accomplished his purpose of creating a universal piano collection.

THE PUBLISHERS.

CLASSIFIED INDEX

LIGHT COMPOSITIONS

ALPHABETICAL INDEX

ALPHABETICAL INDEX

LOURE

J. S. Bach

D.C. al Fine

PRELUDE IN C

(Welltempered Clavichord)

J. S. Bach

BOURRÉE

(from the Second Violin Sonata)

J. S. Bach

MINUET

Tempo di Minuetto

Luigi Boccherini

una corda
un poco animato

RONDO ESPRESSIVO

P. E. Bach

CAPRICE
(from "Alceste")

C.W. Von Gluck

GAVOTTE

F. J. Gossec

Allegretto

BOURRÉE

G. F. Händel

cresc.
f
p
cresc.
Ped.
Ped.
segue
f
f
cresc.
ff
p
Ped.
p
cresc.
Ped.
segue
f
f
cresc.
ff
ritenuto
Ped.

ANDANTE

C.W. von Gluck

SARABANDE

G. Fr. Händel

LE TAMBOURIN

J. P. Rameau

TURKISH MARCH

W. A. Mozart

GIPSY RONDO

J. Haydn

Minore

Maggiore

GAVOTTE

J. B. Lully

Allegro non troppo

Ped. ad lib.

Musette

Fine

sempre legato

sempre legato

D.C. al Fine

MINUET
(from Divertimento No. 1)

W. A. Mozart

SERENADE

J. Haydn

Andante

TEMPO DI BALLO

D. Scarlatti

ADAGIO "MOONLIGHT" SONATA

L. van Beethoven

Adagio sostenuto

sempre pp e con sordini

WEBER'S LAST THOUGHT
(Dernière Pensée Musicale)

C. M. von Weber

FÜR ELISE

L. von Beethoven

Melody by F. H. Himmel

AN ALEXIS

Tr. by J. N. Hummel

Andantino espressivo

MINUET in G

L. van Beethoven

Tempo di Minuet

MOMENT MUSICAL

Fr. Schubert. Op. 94, № 3

UNFINISHED SYMPHONY
(Part of 1st Movement)

Fr. Schubert

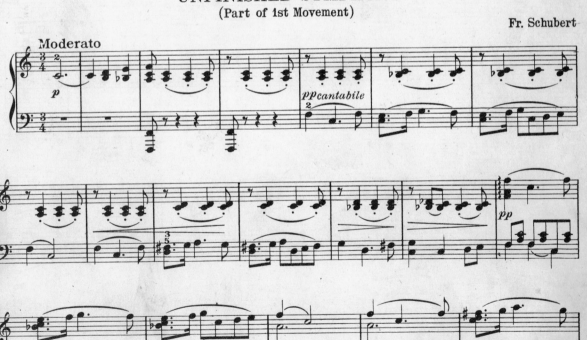

MARCHE MILITAIRE
Op. 51, No 1.

Franz Schubert

Allegro vivace

58

TRIO

simile stacc.

D.C. al Fine

SERENADE

Fr. Schubert

NOCTURNE

John Field

Cantabile, assai lento

"MINUTE" WALTZ

F. Chopin. Op. 6

Molto vivace

PRÉLUDE

F. Chopin. Op. 28, Nº 20

PRELUDE
Op. 28, No 6

Assai lento

Fr. Chopin

NOCTURNE

F. Chopin, Op. 9, Nº 2

PRELUDE
Op.28, No 4

Largo

Fr. Chopin

CONSOLATION

F. Mendelssohn

Adagio non troppo

BERCEUSE

Charles Gounod

NOCTURNE

F. Chopin. Op. 55, № 1.

Andante

LOVE SONG

A. Henselt

Allegretto sostenuto ed amoroso

BERCEUSE

H. Kjerulf

Andante

LA GONDOLA

Etude

A. Henselt Op. 13. No 2

MAZURKA

Op.7, №1.

Fr. Chopin

VALSE

A. Durand, Op. 83, Nº 1

TARENTELLE

Stephen Heller. Op. 85. No 2.

REMEMBRANCE
Op. 68, № 28

R. Schumann

TRÄUMEREI

R. Schumann, Op. 15, Nº 7

Moderato

ROMANZE

Più moto

THE HAPPY FARMER

R. Schumann, Op. 68, № 10

Allegretto animato

WHY?

Robt. Schumann, Op.12, No.3

Lento e delicatamente

SPINNING SONG

F. Mendelssohn

SPRING SONG

F. Mendelssohn

Allegretto grazioso

WEDDING MARCH

(Midsummer Night's Dream)

F. Mendelssohn

Allegro vivace

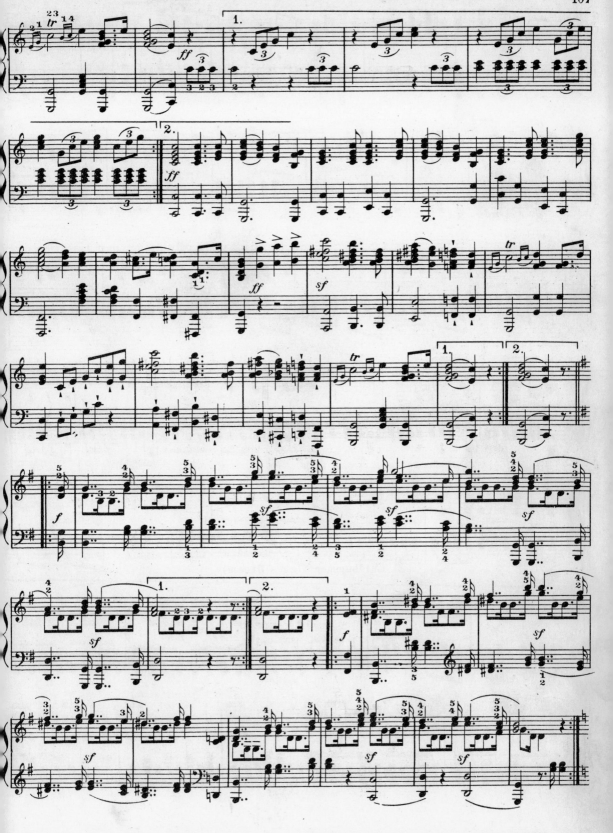

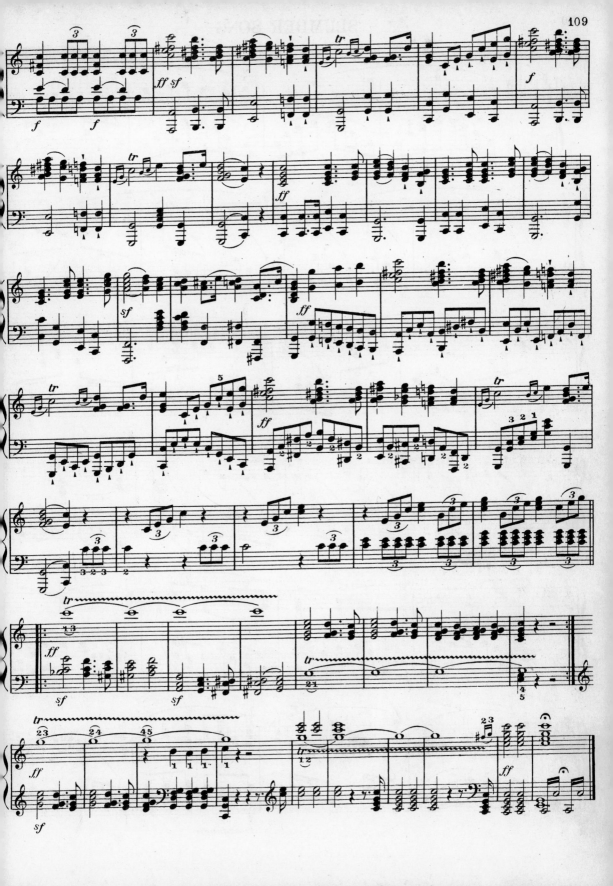

SLUMBER SONG

R. Schumann, Op. 124

Allegretto

WAR MARCH OF THE PRIESTS

From "Athalie"

F. Mendelssohn

Allegro vivace

EVENING SONG

Robert Schumann. Op.23.№4

CONFIDENCE

F. Mendelssohn. Op. 19. N⁰ 4

A LA BIEN AIMÉE

Valse

Ed. Schütt

Valse moderato e cantabile
espressivo e molto dolce

PETITE VALSE

G. Karganoff. Op.10, № 2

AT SUNSET

Allegro con gajezza

E. MacDowell. Op. 28, No 5

CANZONETTA

César Cui

ÉLÉGIE

Andante espressivo

S. Yóuferoff. Op. 1. Nº

BERCEUSE

L. Schytte. Op. 26. No 7

Allegretto moderato

Più mosso

CHANSON TRISTE

P. Tschaikowsky. Op. 40. № 2

Andante

SECOND MAZURKA

Benjamin Godard

EN BERÇANT
(Lullaby)

E. Schütt

RÊVERIE

E. Schütt Op. 34. No 5

Andante cantabile

ROMANCE

A. Rubinstein, Op. 44, No 1

TORÉADOR ET ANDALOUSE

A. Rubinstein. Op. 103, Nº 7

Allegro non troppo

CRESCENDO

Allegretto

Per Lasson

SPANISH DANCE

M. Moszkowski Op. 12, No. 1

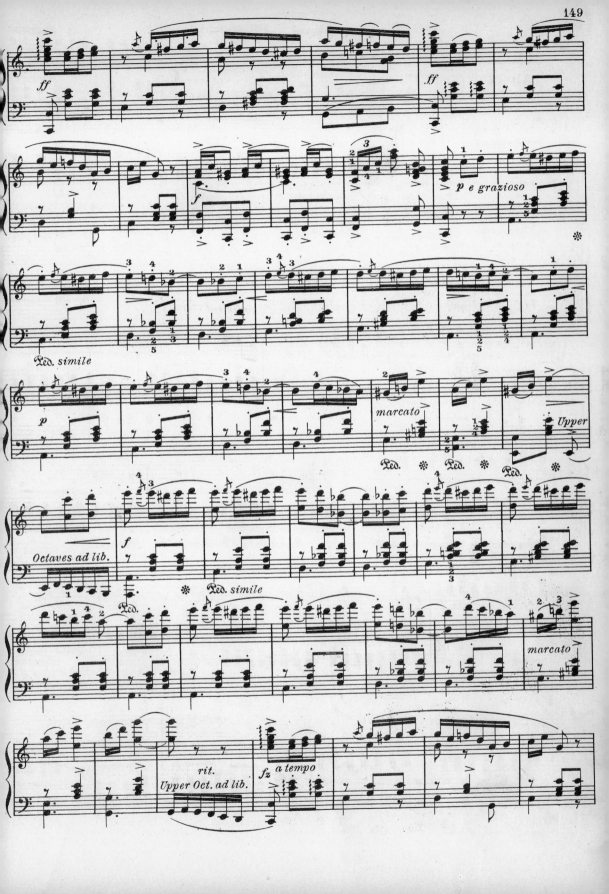

RÊVERIE

André Wormser

Tempo rubato andante *(très soutenu, avec un sentiment rêveur)*

ppp sostenuto molto

Poco mosso

CONSOLATION

Moderato *con espressione e ben legato la melodia*

Th. Leschetizky, Op. 19 No 6

EROTIK

E. Grieg. Op.43, No

THE FLATT'RER

(La Lisonjera)

Cécile Chaminade

RUSTLE OF SPRING

Christian Sinding

SILHOUETTE

A. Dvořak

IN THE WOOD

E. Poldi

CODA

SERENATA

M. Moszkowski

Andante grazioso

PAPILLON
(Butterfly)

E. Grieg

Allegro grazioso

HUMORESQUE

P. Tschaikowsky. Op. 10 Nº 2

Allegretto scherzando

Semplice ma espress

PRÈS DE L'EAU
(By The Sea)

F. Blumenfeld, Op. 38, No 3

Lento, ma non troppo

TRÄUMEREI

Richard Strauss, Op. 9, No 4

ROMANCE

Moderato

A. Jensen

MOMENT MUSICAL

P. Scharwenka

SERENADE

Ole Olsen

THE FLOW'RET

(Forest Idyl No. 1)

E. A. Macdowell

BERCEUSE

G. Delbrück

ROMANCE

J. Raff, Op. 2, No 2

Adagio quasi Andante

CHANT SANS PAROLES

Allegretto grazioso e cantabile

P. Tschaikowsky

VALSE GRACIEUSE

Moderato

A. Dvořák, Op. 54, № 1

Meno mosso, quasi Tempo Iº

Meno mosso, quasi Tempo Primo

MURMURING ZEPHYRS

Murmurando con delicatezza

Adolf Jensen

NOCTURNE
From "Petite Suite"

A. Borodin

ROMANCE SANS PAROLES

G. Fauré. Op. 17. Nº

SCOTCH POEM

E. MacDowell. Op. 31, N̥

Allegro tempestoso

CANZONETTA
(From Violin Concerto)

Benjamin Godard

LE CYGNE
(The Swan)

C. Saint-Saëns

Adagio et legato

PRELUDE

S. Rachmaninoff. Op. 3. No 2

Tempo I

VILLANESCA
Spanish Dance

E. Granados. Op. 5

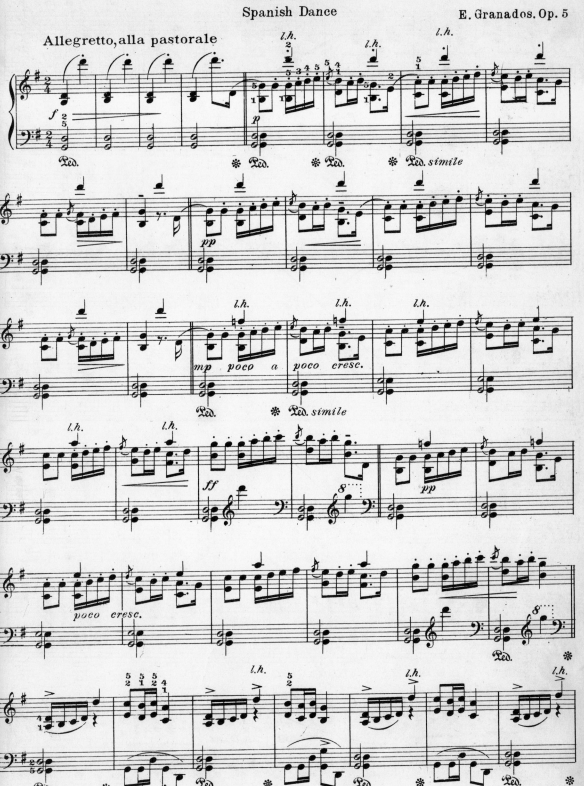

SÉRÉNADE

G. Pierné

Allegretto

HUMORESKE

Anton Dvořák Op. 101, N°

Poco lento et gracioso

ANGELUS
(From "Scenes pittoresques")

J. Massenet

A LOVE DREAM

(Nocturne No. 3)

Franz Liszt

Poco allegro, con affetto

NORWEGIAN DANCE

Allegretto tranquillo e grazioso

Edward Grieg. Op. 35, N

SALUT D'AMOUR
(Love's Greeting)

Edward Elg[ar]

ANITRA'S DANCE

Edward Grieg

Tempo di Mazurka

SCARF DANCE

Valse moderé

Cécile Chaminade

MELODY IN F

A. Rubinstein. Op. 3, Nọ

Moderato

ASE'S DEATH
(Peer Gynt)

Edward Grie

Andante doloroso

con Ped.

ROMANCE

P. Tschaikowsky, Op. 5

PAS DES AMPHORES
(Air de Ballet)

C. Chaminade

p
dim.
rubato
rubato
stringendo
poco cresc
dim.
a tempo
p
rubato
cresc.
rubato
f
Più vivo
accel.
p
cresc.
ff
Ped.

CRADLE SONG
From "Noure and Anitra" Suite

A. Ilyinsky, Op. 13

MURMURING BROOK

E. Poldini

Veloce

MÉLODIE

M. Moszkowski Op.18, No.

BERCEUSE
(Jocelyn)

Benjamin Godard

CONSOLATION

Franz Liszt

Andantino

MAZURKA

C. Saint-Saëns. Op.21, No 1.

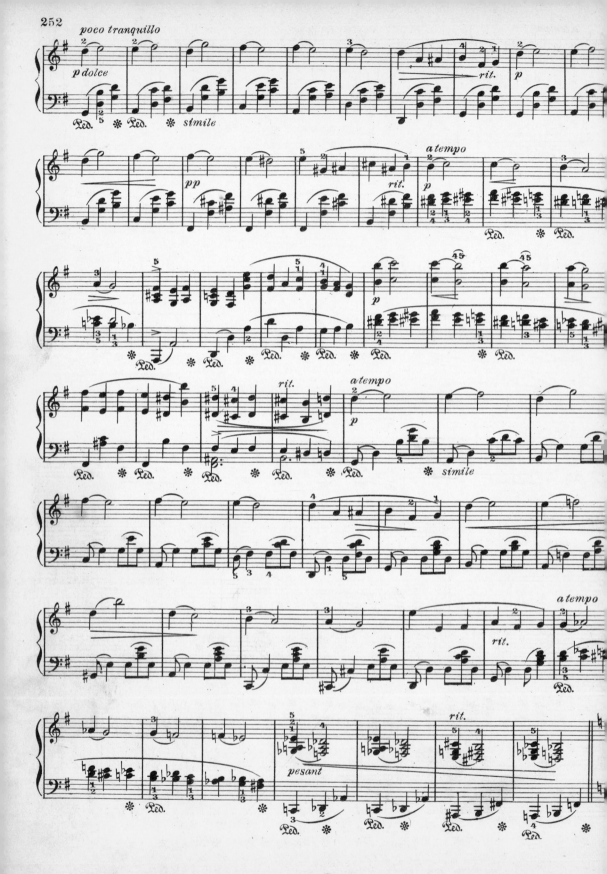

WALTZES
(Selected)

J. Brahms, Op.

MAZURKA
Op. 40, No 2

Erik Meyer-Helmund

RÊVERIE

C. Debussy

MENUET À L'ANTIQUE

Ignace J. Paderewski

Brillante

HUNGARIAN DANCE № 5

J. Brahms

ROMANCE

S. Rachmaninoff

SPRING DANCE

E. Grieg

AU MATIN

Benj. Godard

ALLA MAZURKA

A. Nemerowsky

CABALETTA

Allegro con spirito

Theodore Lack

MÉLODIE

Jules Massenet. Op.1

Lento, ma non troppo

ARABESKE

G. Karganoff

HABANERA

E. Chabrier

POLISH DANCE

Xaver Scharwenka, Op.3, № 1

Allegro

POUPÉE VALSANTE

(Dancing Doll)

Ed. Poldini

F. Drdla

Tranquillo poco Allegro

WARBLINGS AT EVE
Romance
"O Nightingale, that from the blooming spray
Warblest at eve when all the woods are still"

Brinley Richards

Andante con espressione

WAVES OF THE OCEAN

Galop de Salon

Chas. D. Blake

Introduction
Maestoso

Tempo di Galop

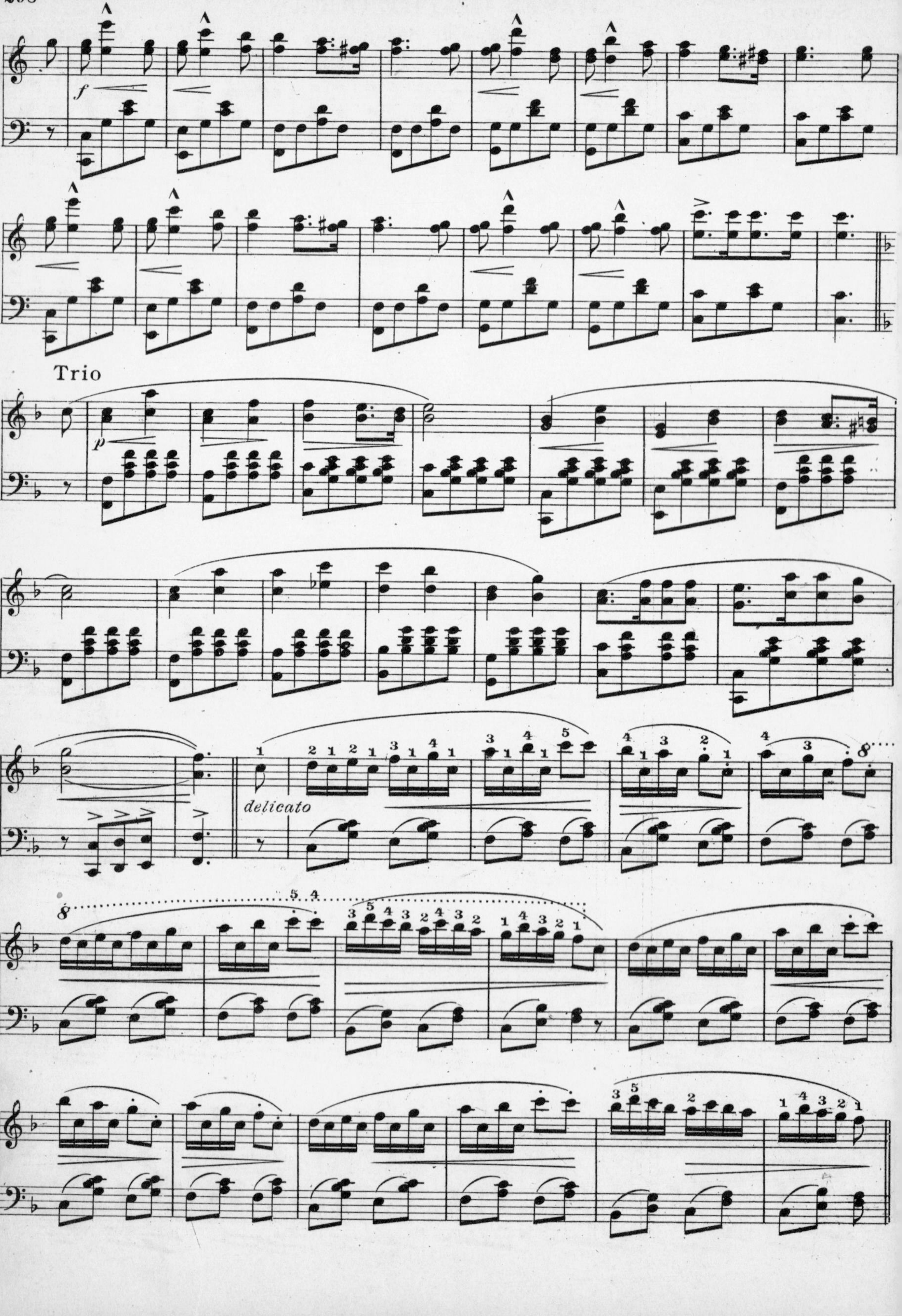
Trio
delicato

Scherzo

Melodia marcato

GOOD NIGHT

A. Loeschhorn

Allegretto tranquillo

SIMPLE AVEU
(Simple Confession)

Francis Thomé

ENTR'ACTE GAVOTTE

E. Gillet

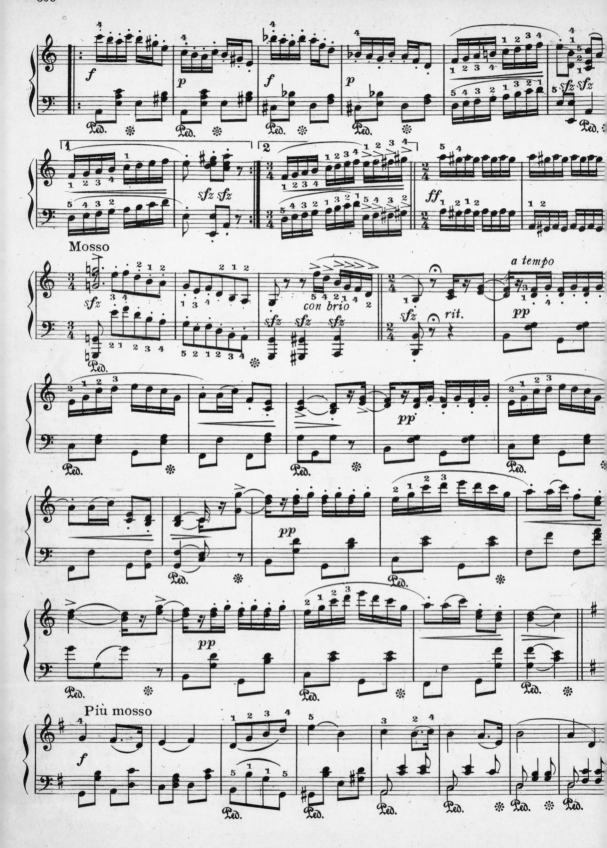

LONGING FOR HOME

Albert Jungmann

THE BLACKSMITH IN THE WOODS

(Forge in the Forest)

Th. Michaelis

Allegretto (Smithy)

Tempo di Polka

Anvil

Ped. ad lib.

Anvil

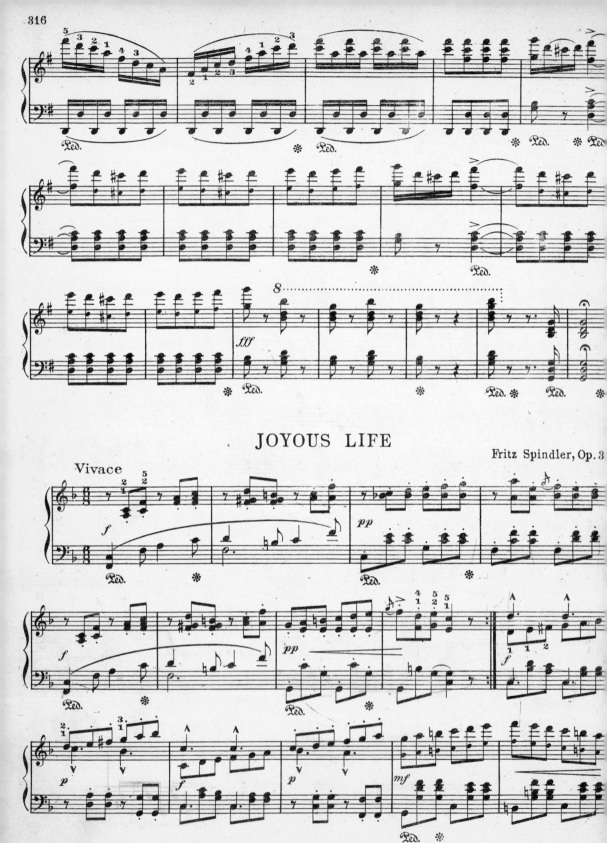

JOYOUS LIFE

Fritz Spindler, Op. 3

Vivace

FIFTH NOCTURNE

M. M. 321

Animato

STEPHANIE

Gavotte

Alphonse Czibulka

Moderato

LOVE'S DREAM AFTER THE BALL

Intermezzo

Returned from the ball, she falls asleep,
and in a charming vision, beholds him to
whom she has given her heart this night.

Tempo di Valse

Alphonse Czibulka

Andante Amoroso
(THE VISION)

Tempo di Valse

poco rit.

in tempo ma un pochettino più lento

ppp poco a poco più lento

morendo

ONE HEART, ONE MIND

Polka Mazurka

Johann Strauss

LONGING

H. Kjerul

THE TURKISH PATROL

Th. Michaelis

Moderato, tempo di marcia

INTERMEZZO RUSSE

Th. Fran...

Tempo di Valse

ESMERALDA

Hesitation Waltz

Carlos de Mesquita

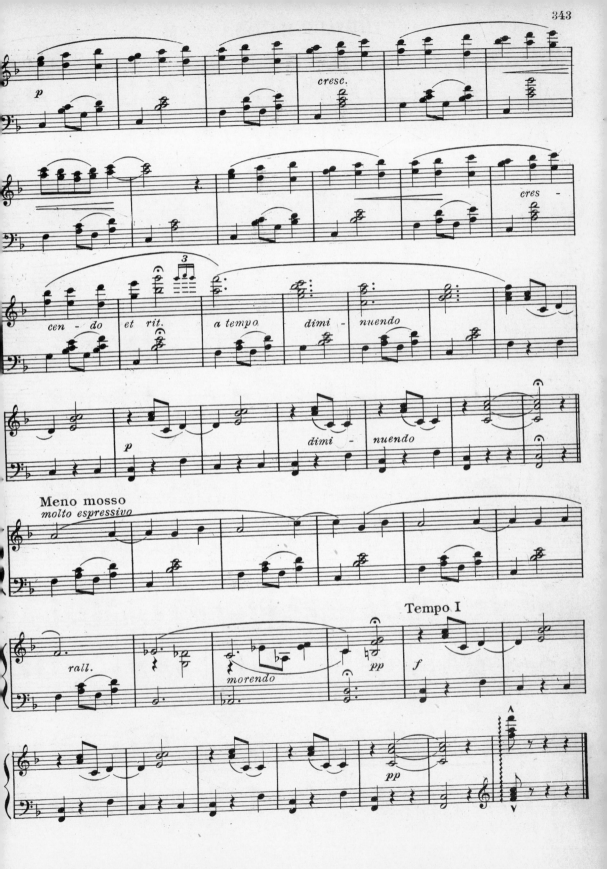

THE ALP-MAID'S DREAM

A. Sabitzl

a tempo
ritard.
un poco più vivo
ritard.
a tempo
ritard.
Andante grave
morendo
ritard.

CHINESE SERENADE

H. Fliege

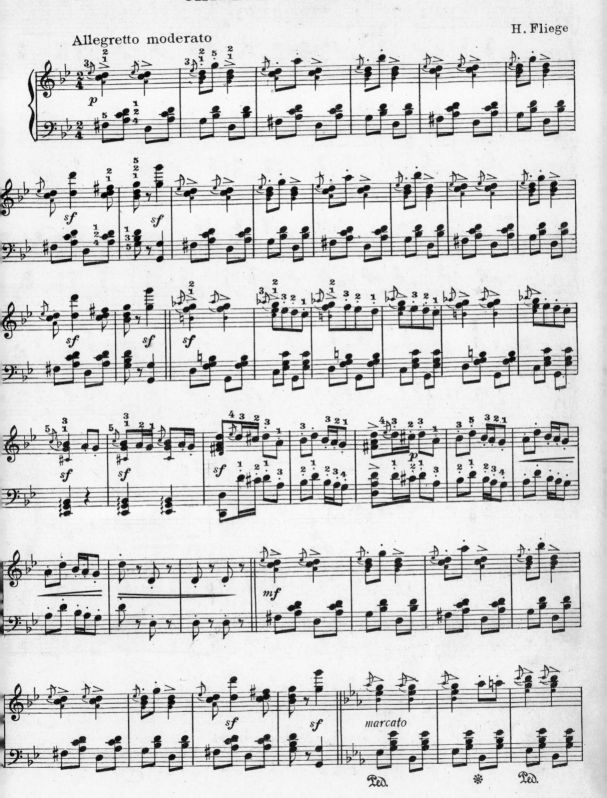

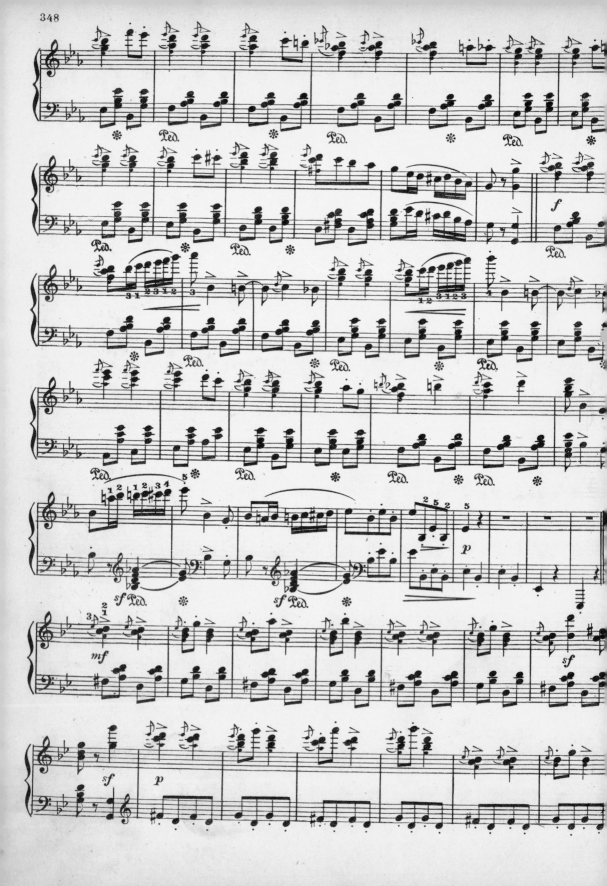

VALSE BLEUE

Alfred Margis

Fin

TRIO

D. S. to Tri

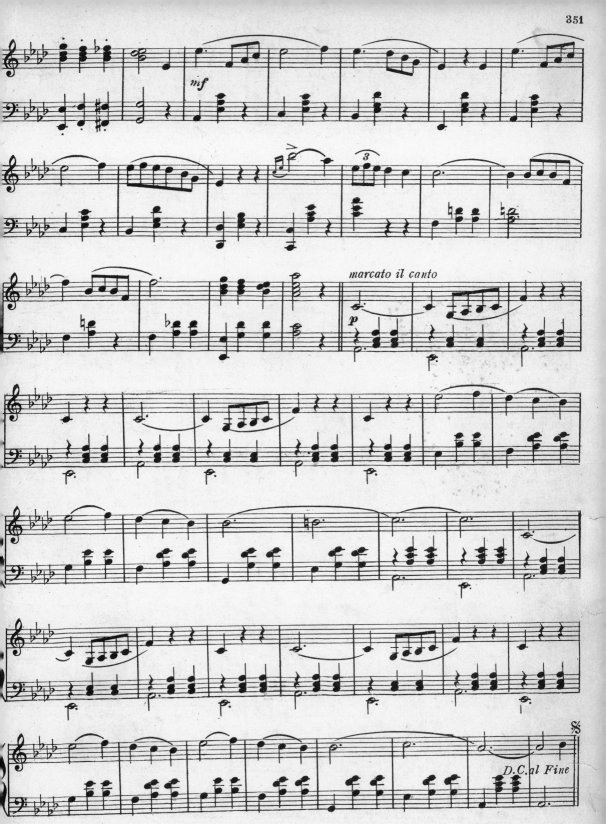

LA PALOMA

S. Yradi

Andante con moto

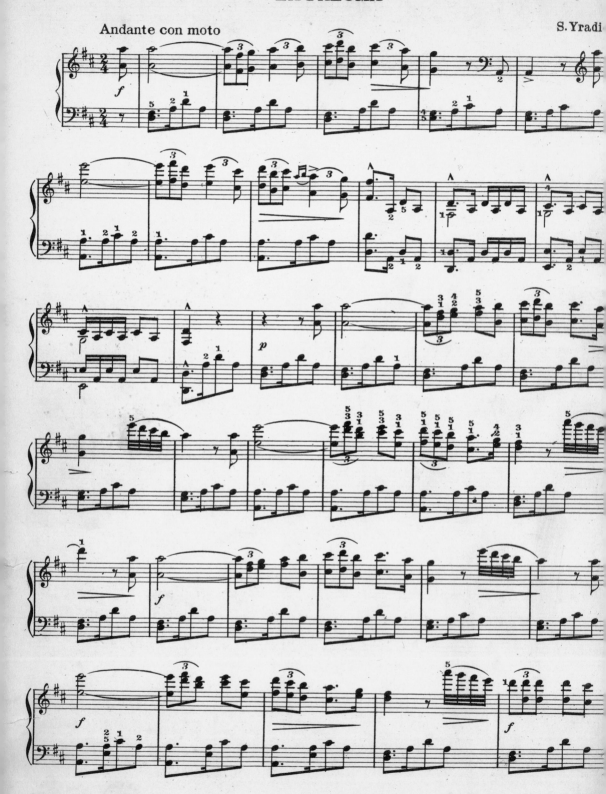

FLOWER SONG

Gustav Lan[ge]

CRADLE SONG

Miska Hauser

LA ZINGANA
Hungarian Dance

C. Bohm

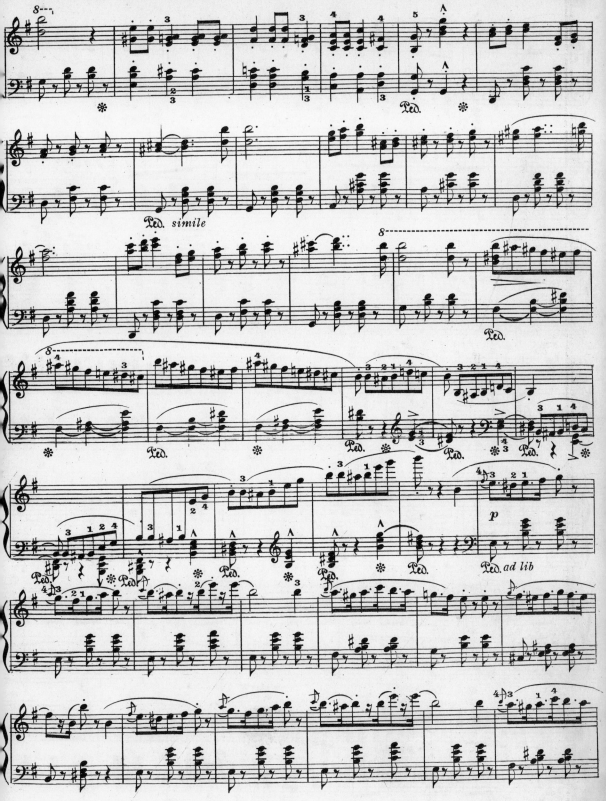

LA FONTAINE
Morceau de Salon

C. Bohm

LOIN DU BAL
(Ball-room Echoes)

Ernest Gillet

Tempo di Valse

LA CZARINE

Russian Mazurka

Tempo di Mazurka

Louis Ganne

CANZONETTA

Victor Hollaender.

Allegretto grazioso

LE SECRET
(Intermezzo)

L. Gautier

THE MAIDEN'S PRAYER

(La Prière d'une Vierge)

Thekla Badarcveszka

CON AMORE

(Mélodie)

Paul Beaumont

Allegretto con grazia

LA CINQUANTAINE
(The Golden Wedding)

Gabriel-Marie

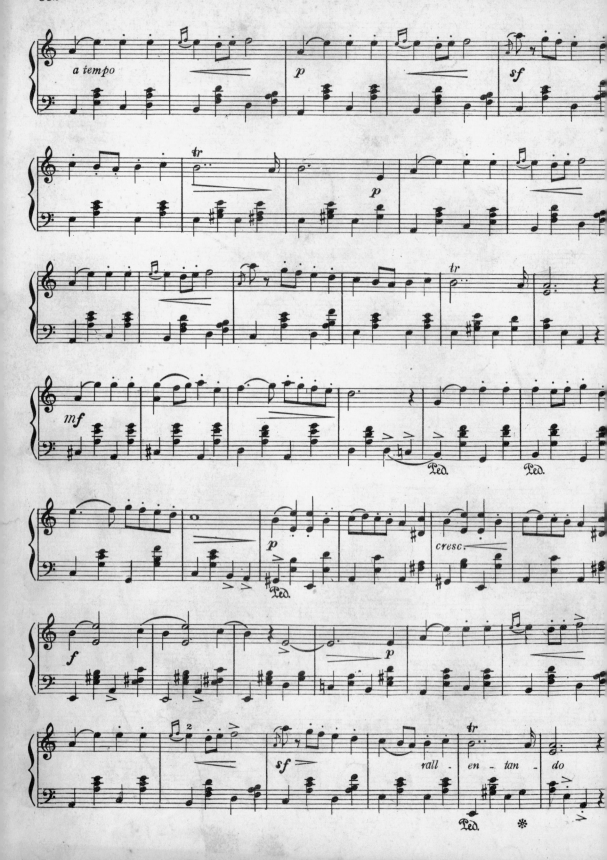

THE DYING POET

Meditation

L. Gottschalk

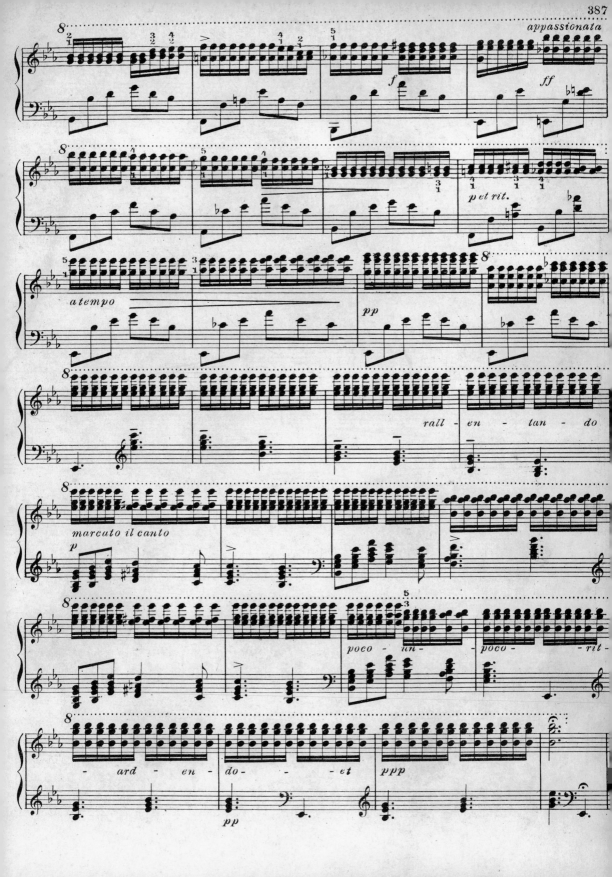

THINE OWN

Gustav Lange

Andante espressione

PURE AS SNOW

Gustave Lange

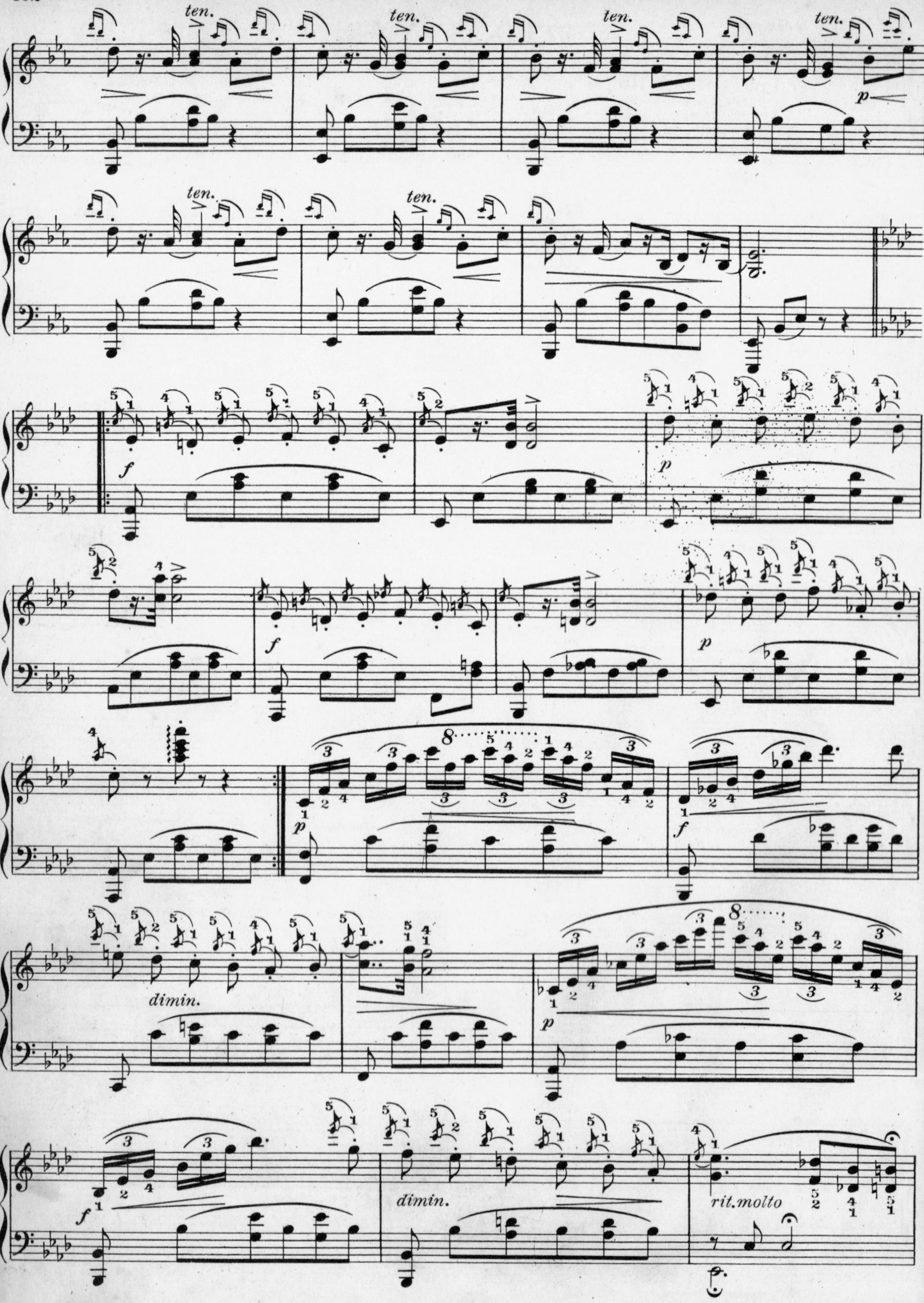
ten.
ten.
ten.
ten.
ten.
ten.
dimin.
dimin.
rit.molto

THE SONG OF THE ROBIN

G. W. Warren

Allegretto pastorale

UNDER THE LEAVES
(Sous la Feuillée)

Fr. Thomé

Poco agitato

ALBUM LEAF

Th. Kirchner

Allegro ma non troppo

LES SYLPHES
Impromptu Valse

G. Bachmann

THE ANGELS' SERENADE

G. Braga

THE LOST CHORD

Sir Arthur Sullivan

Andante moderato

ADESTE FIDELES
Paraphrase

R.Vilbac

A L'ÉGLISE

Choral

G. Pierné, Op.

LARGO

G. F. Hande[l]

AVE MARIA

Fr. Schubert

DEAD MARCH

(From "Saul")

G. F. Handel

THE SHEPHERD BOY

Like some vision olden, of far other time,
When the age was golden, in the young world's prime.
Is thy soft pipe ringing, O lonely shepherd boy;
What song art thou singing, in thy youth and joy?

G. D. Wilson

THE PILGRIM'S SONG OF HOPE

"Hope can here her moonlight vigils keep,
And sing to charm the spirit of the deep.
Swift as yon streamer lights the starry pole,
Her visions warm the Pilgrim's pensive soul."

Campbell.

Edouard Batiste

Transcribed by
Jules de Sivrai

INFLAMMATUS
(From "Stabat Mater")

G. Rossini

THE MONASTERY BELLS

Andantino

Lefébure-Wél

PLEYEL'S HYMN

Transcription

W. J. Westbrook

ANDANTE RELIGIOSO

Francis Thomé

THE LAST HOPE

L. M. Gottschalk

HALLELUJAH CHORUS

(The Messiah)

G. F. Handel

Allegretto moderato

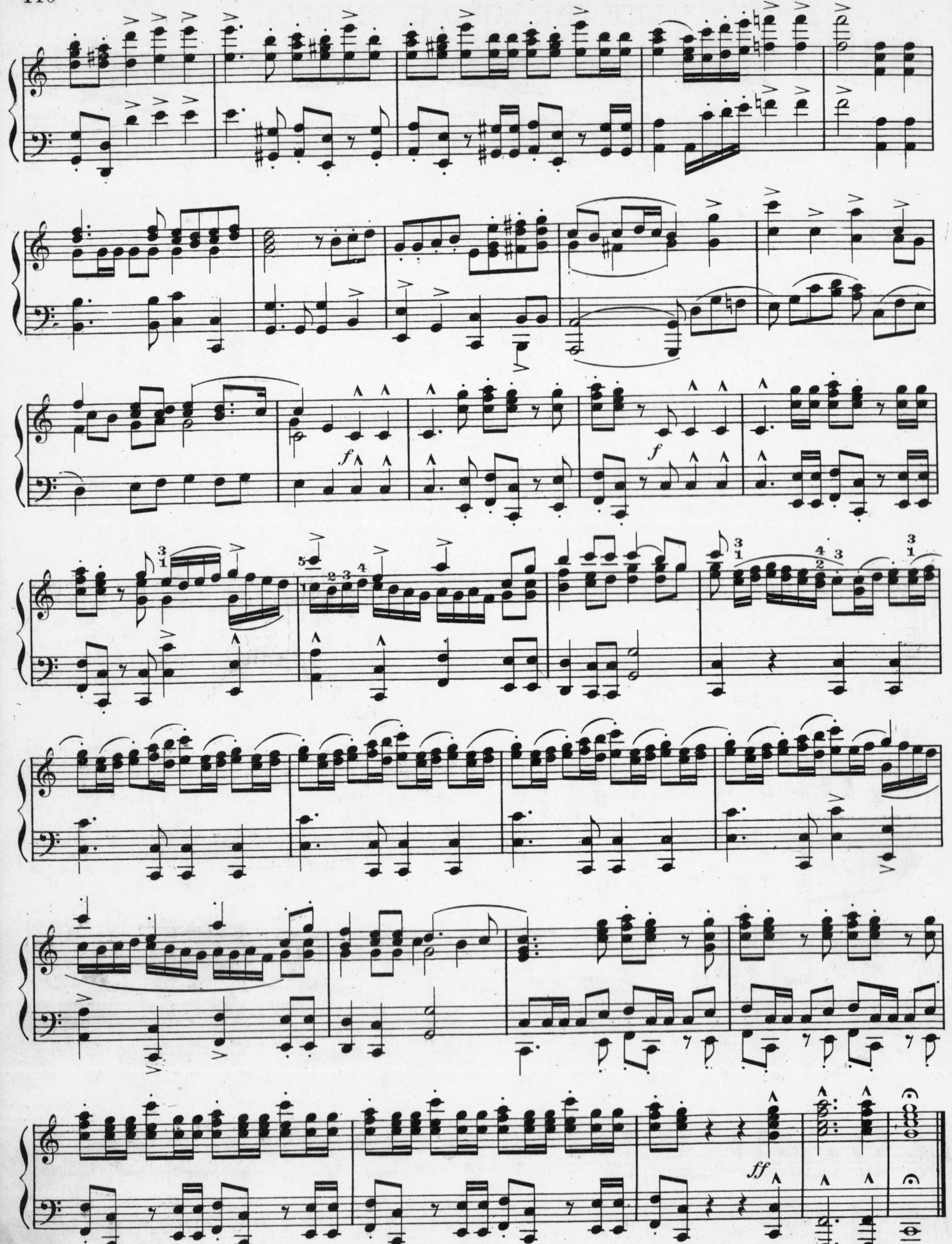
f
f
ff

BUT THE LORD IS MINDFUL
(St. Paul)

F. Mendelssohn

CUJUS ANIMAM

From "Stabat Mater"

G. Rossini

Allegro maestoso

KOL NIDREI

Hebrew melody

FUNERAL MARCH
From Sonata Op. 35

Fr. Chopin

THE GLORY OF GOD IN NATURE

L. Van Beethoven

PRAYER
Op. 48, Nº 1

L. Van Beethoven

Maestoso

THE HEAVENS ARE TELLING

From "The Creation"

J. Haydn

AVE MARIA
Meditation

Bach-Gounod

Andante cantabile

LAST DREAM OF THE VIRGIN

Prelude

J. Massenet

Tempo I

PALM BRANCHES
(Les Rameaux)

J. B. Faure

Andante maestoso

SEXTETTE
(Lucia di Lammermoor)

G. Donizetti

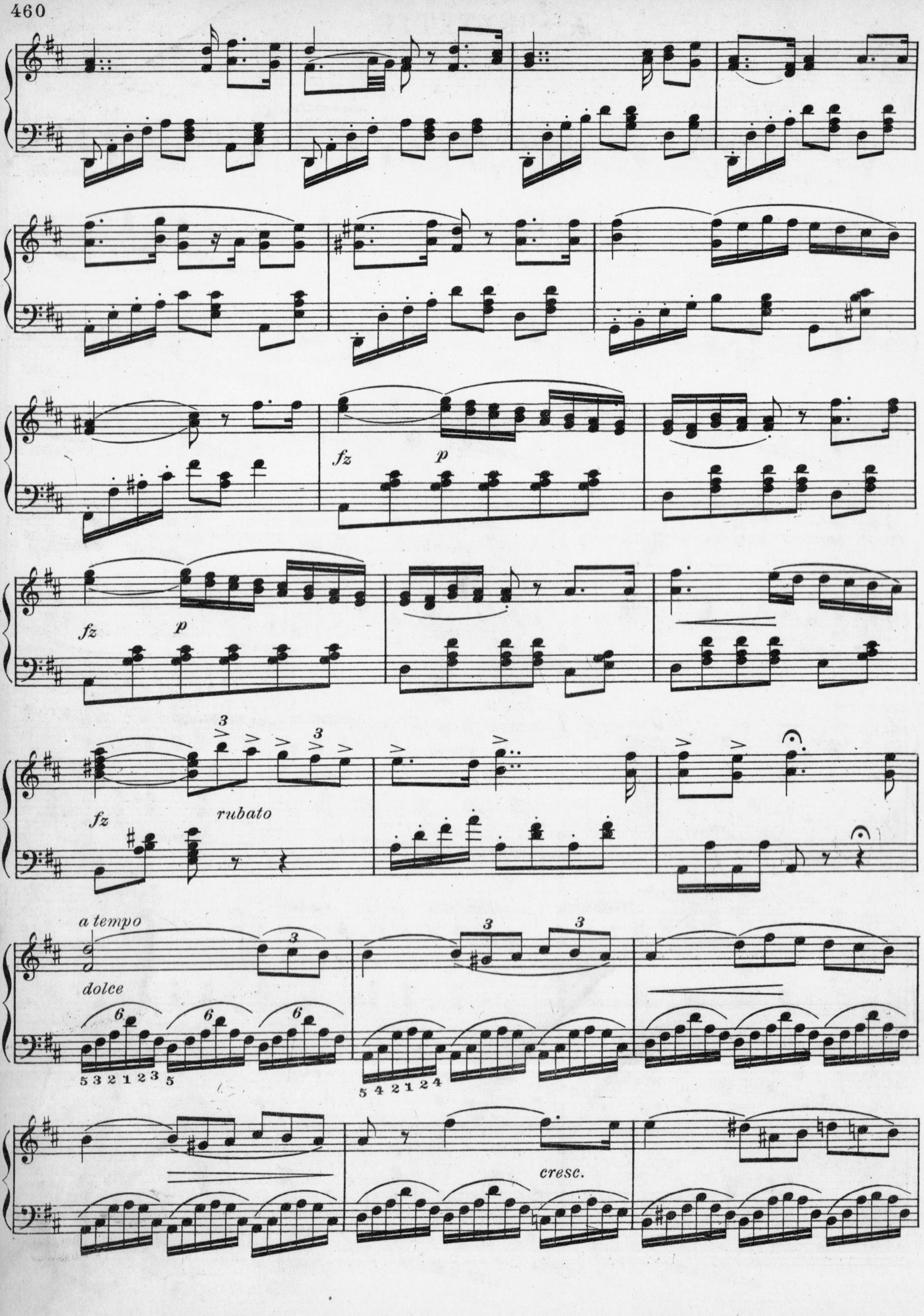
fz
p
fz
p
fz
rubato
a tempo
dolce
cresc.

VALSE LENTE
(Coppelia)

L. Delibes

Valse Tempo

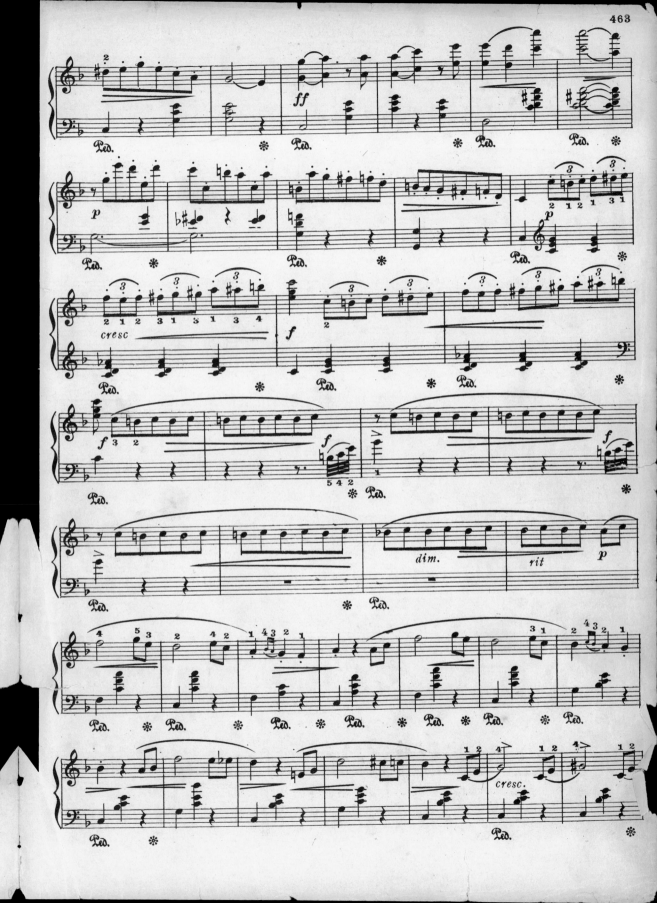

SICILIANA
(Cavalleria Rusticana)

P. Mascagni

Andante Sostenuto
(Siciliana)

WALTZ
(Faust)

Ch. Gounod

Tempo di Valse

GRAND MARCH
(Aïda)

G. Verdi

Tempo di Marcia

MY HEART AT THY SWEET VOICE

(Samson and Delilah)

C. Saint-Saëns

474 Poco più lento

GRAND MARCH
(Norma)

Tempo di Marcia

V. Bellini

ARAGONAISE
(Le Cid)

Jules Massenet

MISERERE
(Il Trovatore)

G. Verdi

MINUET
(Don Juan)

Andante ma non troppo

W. A. Mozart

CORONATION MARCH

From "Le Prophete"

G. Meyerbeer

Tempo di Marcia molto maestoso

INTERMEZZO
(Cavalleria Rusticana)

P. Mascagni

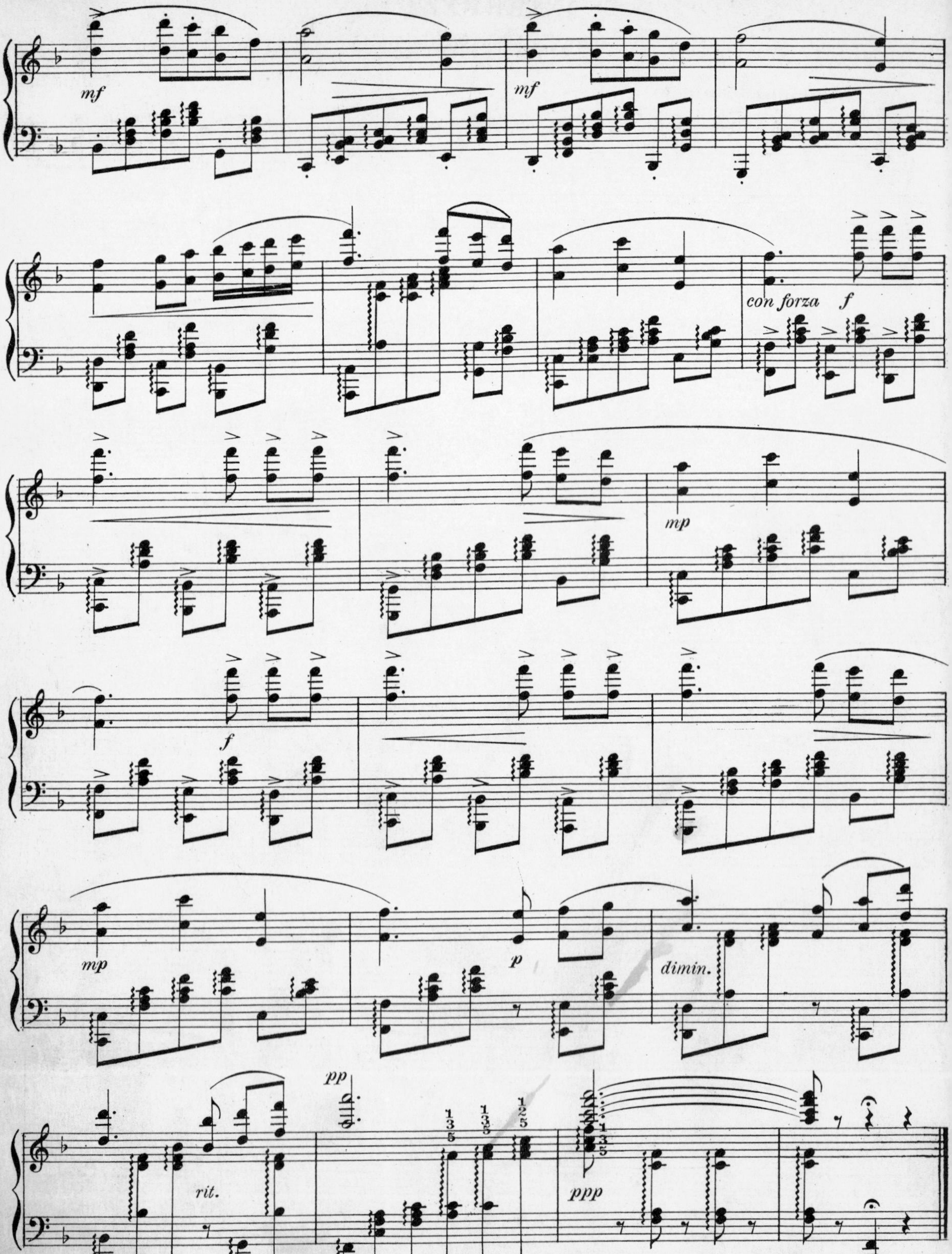
mf
mf
con forza
f
mp
f
mp
p
dimin.
rit.
pp
ppp

QUARTET
(Rigoletto)

G. Verdi

DRINKING SONG
(La Traviata)

G. Verdi

CELESTE AÏDA

(Aïda)

G. Verdi

BRIDAL MARCH

(Lohengrin)

R. Wagner

Con moto moderato

TO THE EVENING STAR

(Tannhäuser)

R. Wagner

Andante sostenuto

GRAND MARCH
(Tannhäuser)

R. Wagner

Tempo di Marcia maestoso

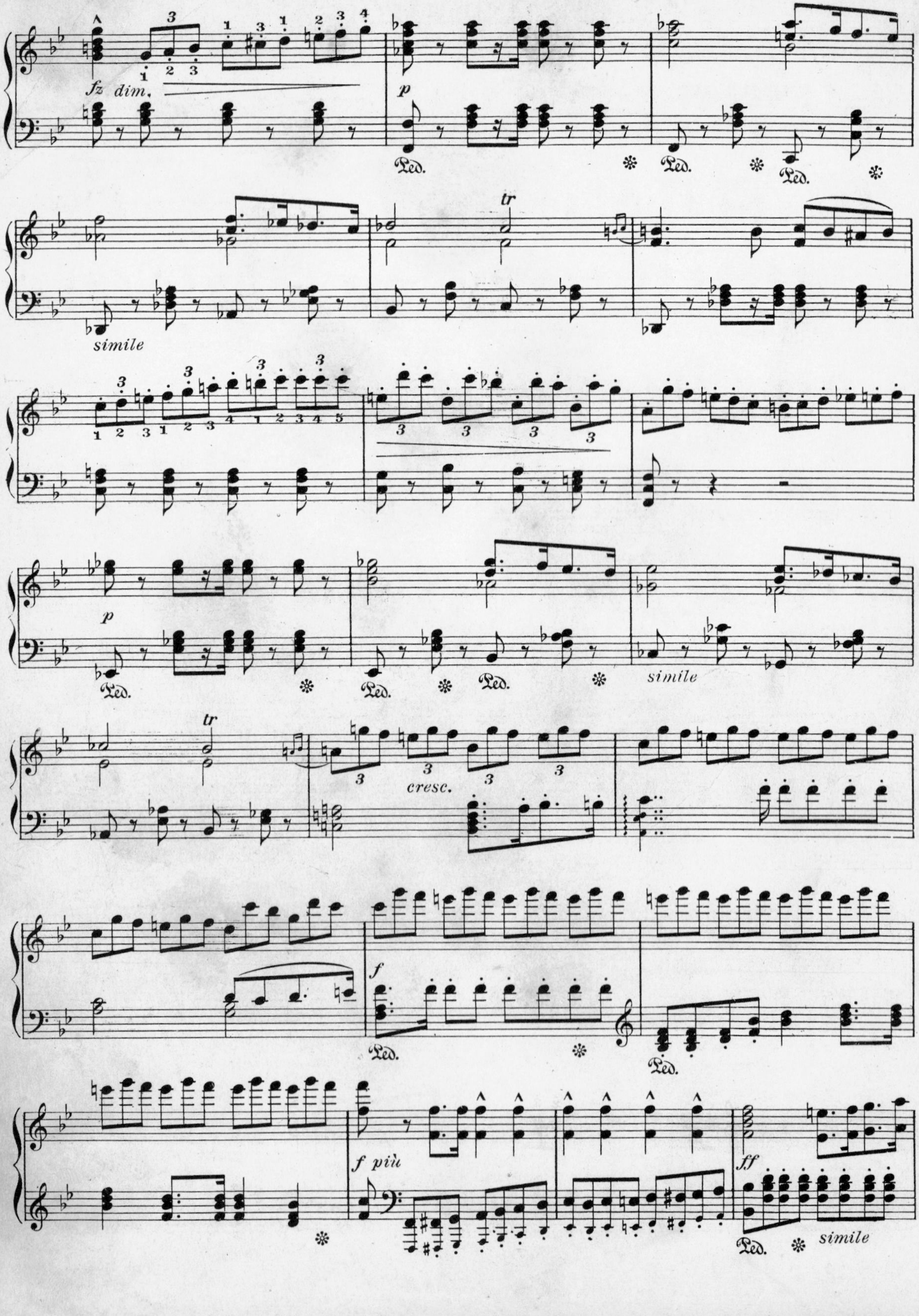
fz dim.
p
Ped.
simile
tr
cresc.
f
f più
ff

Maestoso (Overture)

WILLIAM TELL
(Excerpts)

G. Rossini

Andante (Overture)

Allegro (Finale Overture)

GAVOTTE
(Mignon)

A. Thomas

Tempo di Gavotte.

PIZZICATO

("Sylvia" Ballet)

Leo Delibes

HABANERA

(Carmen)

G. Bizet

DANCE OF THE HOURS
(La Gioconda)

A. Ponchielli

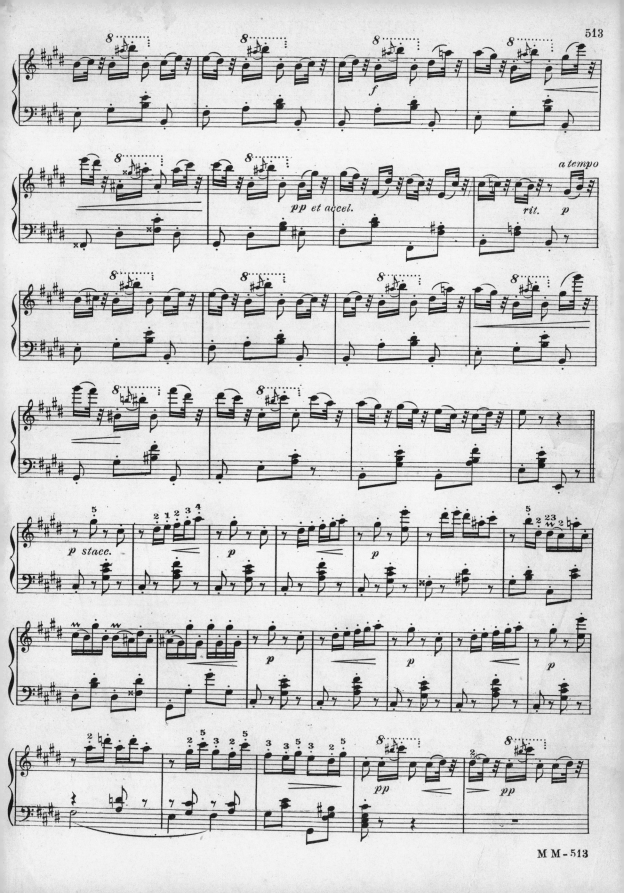

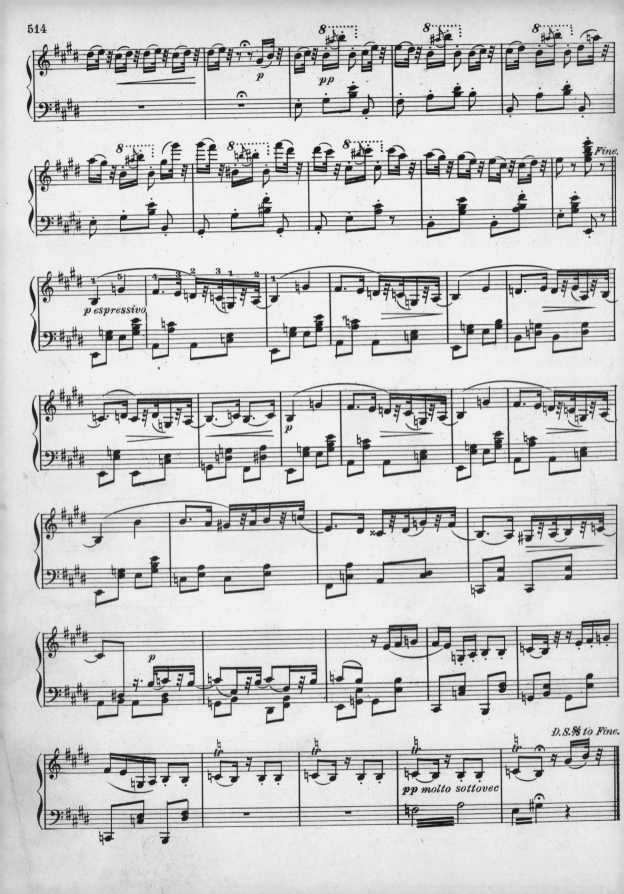

ENTR'ACTE
(from Rosamunde)

Franz Schubert

PRAYER
(The Hunter)

C. M. von Weber

Adagio

BARCAROLLE
(Tales of Hoffman)

J. Offenbach

Bein marque le chant.

Ped. ✱

simile

f

p

sempre piu   dolce   morendo

ppp   ppp

ANVIL CHORUS
(Il Trovatore)

G. Verdi

PRAYER
(Hansel and Gretel)

E. Humperdinck

POET AND PEASANT

F. von Suppé

Andante maestoso (Overture)

A Concise Dictionary of Musical Terms

Aban'don. Without restraint.

Acceleran'do. Increasing the speed.

Ada'gio. Slow, faster than lar'go and slower than andan'te.

Ad Lib'itum. At will, play to suit your own idea of the time.

Agita'to. Agitated, hurried.

Al Fine. To the end.

Allegret'to. Cheerfully and quickly.

Alle'gro. Quickly, vivaciously.

Alle'gro Agita'to. Quickly and with agitation.

Alle'gro Con Bri'o. Quickly with brilliancy.

Alle'gro Con Fuo'co. Quickly and full of fire.

Alle'gro Modera'to. Moderately quick.

Alle'gro non Trop'po. Not too quickly.

Alle'gro Viva'ce. Very rapidly.

Al Se'gno. "Go back to the sign," which means that the player must return to the sign :S: previously marked above some bar of the composition, and play from that measure to the word "Fine" or the mark ⌒

Andan'te. In a moderate tempo, with expression and grace.

Andan'te Canta'bile. Slowly and in a singing style.

Andan'te Con Mo'to. With an easy motion.

Andan'te ma non Trop'po. Not too slow.

Andanti'no. Less slow than "Andante."

Anima'to. With life and spirit, animatedly.

A po'co. Gradually.

A po co a po'co. Little by little.

A po'co pi'u Len'to. A little slower.

Appassiona'to. Passionately.

Assa'i. Very, extremely.

A Tem'po. In time.

Ben Marca'to. Well marked or accented.

Ben Tenu'to. Well sustained.

Brillan'te. Brilliantly.

Calan'do. Gradually diminishing in tone and growing slower in time.

Canta'bile. In a singing style.

Chantant'. In a melodious or singing style.

Con Amo're. With tenderness.

Con An'ima. With animation.

Con Bri'o. With spirit.

Con Calo're. With fire.

Con Esp. Abbreviation for "Con Expressione."

Cresc. Abbreviation for "Crescendo."

Crescen'do. Increase in power of tone.

Crescen'do al diminuen'do. Increase and then diminish the tone.

D. C. Abbreviation for "Da Capo."

Da Ca'po. From the beginning.

Da Ca'po al Fi'ne. Return to the beginning and play as far as the word "Fine."

D. S. Abbreviation for "Dal Segno."

Dal Se'gno. Repeat from the sign : S :-

Dal Se'gno Alla Fi'ne. Repeat from the sign :S: to the word "Fine."

Deci'so. In a decided manner.

Decrescen'do. Gradually diminish in power of tone.

Delibera'to. Deliberately.

Delica'to. Delicately.

Dim. Abbreviation for "Diminuen'do."

Diminuen'do. Decreasing gradually the power of the tone.

Dol'ce. Sweetly and softly.

Dol'ce e Canta'bile. Sweetly in a singing style.

Douce'ment. Sweetly and softly.

Elegan'te. Elegant.

Ener'gico. Vigorous, forcible.

Espress. Abbreviation for "Espressivo."

Espressi'vo. Expressive.

F. Abbreviation for "Forte."

FF. Abbreviation for "Fortissimo."

FFF. Abbreviation for "Fortississimo."

Facilement'. With facility.

For'te. Loud.

Fortis'simo. Very loud.

Fortissis'simo. As loud as possible.

Forzan'do. Strongly accenting certain notes or chords.

Fuo'co. Fire, passion.

Furio'so. Furious, mad.

Gai'ement. Gayly, merrily.

Genti'le. Elegant, graceful.

Gioco'so. Sportively.

Glissan'do. In a gliding manner, accomplished on the piano by drawing the fingers rapidly over the keyboard.

Grandio'so. Grand, noble.

Grave. A slow, solemn movement.

Habane'ra. A slow Spanish dance.

Humoreske'. A playful musical composition.

I'dyl. A musical composition in pastoral style.

Introduc'tion. The first measures in a musical composition which prepare one for the main part.

Lagrimo'so. Tearful.

Lamentan'do. Lamenting.

Larghet'to. Not quite as slow as "Largo."

Lar'go. Solemn and slow.

Lar'go ma non Trop po. Slow, but not too much so.

Lega'to. In a smooth manner, slurred.

Legere'ment. Lightly, nimbly.

Leggier'o. Light and swift.

Lent. Slow.

Lentemen te. Slowly.

L'istes'so. Lisping or whispering.

Maesto'so. Majestic, dignified.

Marc. Abbreviation for "Marcato."

Marca'to. Strongly accented.

Me'no. Less.

Me'no Mosso. Slower.

Mezzo For'te. Moderately loud.

Mezzo Pia'no. Moderately soft.

Mo'bile. Movable, changeable.

Modera'to. Moderately.

Morceau'. A choice musical composition.

No'bile. Noble, impressive.

Noc'turne. A dreamy, romantic composition.

Non. "No."

Peu. Little.

Peu a Peu. Little by little.

Piace're. (A). At pleasure.

Piano. Soft.

PP. Abbreviation for "Pianissimo."

Pianissimo. Very soft.

PPP. Abbreviation for "Pianississimo."

Pianississimo. As soft as possible.

Pi'u. More.

Pi'u Alle'gro. More quickly.

Pi'u For'te. Louder.

Pi'u Len'to. More slowly.

Pi'u Mos'so. More quickly.

Pi'u Pia'no. More softly.

Pi'u Pres'to. More rapidly.

Pi'u Vi'vo. More lively.

Plus Anime'. With more animation.

Plus Len'tement. More slowly.

Po'co. Little.

Po'co Ada'gio. A little slower.

Po'co Alle'gro. A little faster.

Po'co Anima'to. A little more animated.

Po'co a po'co. By degrees.

Po'co a po'co Crescen'do. Gradually louder and louder.

Po'co a po'co Diminuen'do. Gradually softer and softer.

Po'co pi'u Mos'so. A little faster.

Pres'to. Quickly, rapidly.

Pres'to Assai. Very quick.

Pres'to ma non Trop'po. Not too quick.

Qua'si Allegret'to. Like an "Allegretto."

Qua'si Andan'te. Like an "Andante."

Qua'si Pres'to. Like a "Presto."

Qua'si Un Fanta'sia. Like a "Fantasy."

Rall. Abbreviation for "Rallentando."

Rallentan'do. Gradually slower.

Religio'so. Religiously.

R. H. Abbreviation for "Right Hand."

Risolu'to. Resolutely, boldly.

Ritard. Abbreviation for "Ritardando."

Ritardan'do. Holding back the time.

Riten. or Rit. Abbreviation for "Ritenuto."

Ritenu'to. Held back.

Ruba'to. Taking part of the rightful time-duration of one note and giving it to another.

Scherzan'do. In a playful manner.

Scher'zo. A playful composition.

Se'gno. A sign :S: indicating a return to some previous part of the composition.

Semp. Abbreviation for "Sempre."

Sem'pre. Always, ever to a greater degree.

Sem'pre For'te. Ever loud.

Sem'pre Lega'to. Ever legato.

Sem'pre Pia'no. Ever piano.

Sem'pre P'iu Fort'e. Ever louder.

Sem'pre P'iu Pres'to. Ever faster.

Sem'pre Ritardan'do. Ever slower.

Sem'pre Stacca'to. Ever staccato.

Sentimen'to. With sentiment.

SFZ. Abbreviation for "Sforzando."

Sforzan'do. Play some particular note with special accent.

Sost. Abbreviation for "Sostenuto."

Sostenu'to. Sustained.

Stacc. Abbreviation for "Staccato."

Stacca'to. Detached playing of notes.

String. Abbreviation for "Stringendo."

Stringen'do. Accelerating the time.

Tem'po. Musical time.

Tem. 1⁰. Abbreviation for "Tempo Primo."

Tem'po Pri'mo. First or original time as marked on a piece.

Ten. Abbreviation for "Tento."

Ten'uto. Sustained, held.

Tres. Very.

Tres Anime'. Very lively.

Tres Fort. Very loud.

Tres Len'te. Very slow.

Tres Pia'no. Very soft.

Tres Vi'te. Very Quick.

Velo'ce. Swiftly.

Vif. Lively, briskly.

Vigoro'so. Vigorously.

Viva'ce. Lively, vivaciously.

Vi'vo. Animated.

A BRIEF BIOGRAPHICAL PRONOUNCING DICTIONARY OF THE COMPOSERS IN THIS VOLUME

BACH, JOHANN SEBASTIAN (Barck), Classical, 1685-1750.

BACH, PHILIP EMANUEL (Barck), Classical, 1714-88.

BACHMANN, GEORGES (Barck-marn), French, 1848-94.

BADARCVESZKA, TECLA (Bad-a-sev-ska), Polish, 1838-62.

BATISTE, EDWARD (Ba-teest), French, 1820-76.

BEAUMONT, PAUL (Bow-mon), French, 1853—

BEETHOVEN, L. VAN (Bay-toe-ven), Classical, 1770-1827.

BELLINI, VINCENZO (Bell-een-ee), Italian, 1802-35.

BIZET, GEORGES (Beet-zay), French, 1838-75.

BLAKE, CHARLES D., American, 1847—

BLUMENFELD, F. (Bloo-men-feld), Russian, 1863—

BOCCHERINI, LUIGI (Bock-air-een-ee), Italian, 1743-1805.

BOHM, CARL (Bowhm), Light, 1844—

BORODIN, A. (Bor-o-deen), Russian, 1834-1887.

BRAGA, GAETANO (Brar-ga), Italian, 1829-1911.

BRAHMS, JOHANNES (Brarms), Modern, 1833-97.

CHABRIER, E. (Sha-bree-air), French, 1842-1894.

CHAMINADE, CECÍLE (Sham-ee-nard), French, 1861.

CHOPIN, FREDERIC (Sho-parng), Polish, 1810-49.

CUI, CESAR (Q-ee), Russian, 1835.

CZIBULKA, ALPHONSE (Si-bull-ka), Hungarian, 1842-94.

DEBUSSY, C. (Dee-boo-see), French, 1862-1918.

DELIBES, L. (De-leeb), French, 1836-91.

DONIZETTI, GAETANO (Don-i-zet-ti), Italian, 1797-1848.

DURAND, AUGUSTE (Doo-rann), French, 1830-1909.

DVOŘÁK, ANTONIN (Vor-shak), Bohemian, 1841-1904.

ELGAR, SIR EDWARD, English, 1857—

FAURÉ, GABRIEL (Four-ay), French, 1830—

FAURE, J. BAPTISTE (Four), French, 1830—

FIELD, JOHN, Irish, 1782-1837.

FRANKE, TH. (Frank-ay), French.

GANNE, LOUIS (Gan), French, 1862—

GAUTIER, LOUIS (Gort-yea), French.

GILLET, ERNEST (Gill-ay), French, 1856—

GLUCK, C. W. VON (Glook), Classical, 1714-87.

GODARD, BENJAMIN (Go-dar), French, 1849-95.

GOSSEC, JOSEPH (Gos-seck), Dutch, 1734-1829.

GOTTSCHALK, LOUIS (Gotts-chalk), American, 1829-69.

GOUNOD, CHARLES (Goo-no), French, 1818-93.

GRANADOS, E. (Gran-ar-doss), Spanish.

GRIEG, EDWARD (Greeg), Norwegian, 1843-1907.

HANDEL, G. F. (Hen-del), Classical, 1685-1759.

HAUSER, MISKA (How-zer), Hungarian, 1822-87.

HAYDN, JOSEPH (Hi-den), Classical, 1732-1809.

HELLER, STEPHEN (Hel-ler), Hungarian, 1815-88.

HENSELT, ADOLF (Hen-selt), Bavarian, 1814-89.

HOLLAENDER, VICTOR (Hol-len-der), Light Opera, 1866—

HUMMEL, J. N. (Hoom-mel), Classical, 1778-1837.

HUMPERDINCK, E. (Hum-per-dink), 1854—

ILYINSKI, ALEXANDER (Ill-yin-ski), Russian, 1859—

JENSEN, A. (Yen-sen), 1837-79.

JUNGMANN, ALBERT (Yung-marn), 1824-92.

KARGANOFF, GENARI (Car-garn-off), Russian, 1858-90.

KIRCHNER, THEODORE (Keerk-ner), 1824-1903.

KJERULF, HALFDAN (Ki-rulf), Norwegian, 1815-1868.

LABITZKY, JOSEPH (La-bit-ski), 1802-81.

LACK, THEODORE (Larck), French, 1846—

LANGE, G. (Larng-e), 1830-89.

LEFÉBURE-WÉLY (Lef-ay-boor-way-lee), French, 1817-69.

LESCHETIZKY, THEODORE (Lesh-e-tits-kee), Polish, 1830.

LEYBACH, IGNACE (Lay-barck), French, 1817-91.

LISZT, FRANZ (List), Hungarian, 1811-86.

LULLY, J. B. (Lool-ly), Italian, 1633-1687.

MACDOWELL, EDWARD (Mac-Dow-el), American, 1861-1908.

MARGIS, A. (Mar-jis), French, 1874—

MASCAGNI, PIETRO (Mars-karn-yee), Italian 1863—

MASSENET, JULES (Mass-sen-ay), French, 1842-1912.

MENDELSSOHN, FELIX (Men-dell-sown), Classical, 1809-47.

MESQUITA, C. (May-ski-tar), Spanish.

MEYERBEER, GIACOMO (Mi-er-beer), 1791-1864.

MEYER-HELMUD, ERIK (Mi-er-Hell-mund), Russian, 1861—

MICHAELIS, TH. (Mi-kay-lees), 1831-1887.

MOSZKOWSKI, MORITZ (Mos-kof-ski), 1854—

MOZART, W. A. (Mot-zart), Classical, 1756-91.

NEMEROWSKY, A. (Nem-er-ow-skee), Russian.

OFFENBACH, JACQUES (Of-fen-barck), French, 1819-1880.

OLSEN, O. (Ole-sen), Norwegian, 1850—

PADEREWSKI, IGNACE (Pad-ref-skee), Polish, 1859—

PIERNÉ, GABRIEL (Pee-air-nay), French, 1863—

POLDINI, EDWARD (Poll-dee-nee), 1869—

PONCHIELLI, AMILCARE (Pong-kee-el-lee), Italian, 1834-86.

RACHMANINOFF, SERGEI (Rarck-marn-i-noff), Russian, 1873—

RAFF, J. (Rarf), 1822-82.

RAMEAU, J. P. (Ra-mo), French, 1683-1764.

RICHARDS, BRINLEY, Welsh, 1817-85.

ROSSINI, G. (Row-seen-ee), Italian, 1792-1868.

RUBINSTEIN, ANTON (Roo-bin-stein), Russian, 1830-94.

SAINT-SAËNS, CAMILLE (San-Sans), French, 1835—

SCARLATTI, D. (Scar-lat-ti), Italian, 1683-1757.

SCHARWENKA, PHILIPP (Shar-veng-ka), 1847—

SCHARWENKA, XAVER (Shar-veng-ka), 1850—

SCHUBERT, FRANZ (Shoo-bert), 1797-1828.

SCHUMANN, ROBERT (Shoo-marn), 1810-56.

SCHÜTT, EDWARD (Shuett), Russian, 1856—

SCHYTTE, LUDWIG (Shi-tay), Danish, 1850—

SINDING, CHRISTIAN (Sin-ding), Norwegian, 1856—

SPINDLER, F. (Spin-dler), 1817-1906.

STRAUSS, J. (Strowss), 1825-99.

STRAUSS, RICHARD (Strowss), 1864—

SULLIVAN, SIR ARTHUR, English, 1842-1900.

SUPPE, FRANZ VON (Soo-pay), 1820-95.

THOMAS, AMBROISE, French, 1811-96.

THOMÉ, FRANCIS (Tho-may), French, 1850-1909.

TSCHAIKOWSKY, PETER (Cha-cow-skee), Russian, 1840-93.

VERDI, G. (Ver-di), Italian, 1813-1901.

WAGNER, RICHARD (Warg-ner), 1813-83.

WARREN, G. W., American, 1828.

WEBER, C. M. VON, 1786-1826.

WESTBROOK, A., English, 1831-94.

WILSON, G. D., American.

WORMSER, A. (Worm-ser), French, 1851—

YÓUFEROFF, S. (You-fare-off), Russian.

YRADIER, S. (Rad-yehr), Spanish.

COMPOSER'S INDEX